HISTORY & GEOGRAPHY
THE TOOLS OF THE GEOGRAPHER

CONTENTS

Author:	**Charles L. Fash, M.A.Ed.**
Editor-in-Chief:	Richard W. Wheeler, M.A.Ed.
Editor:	Richard R. Andersen, M.A.
Consulting Editor	Howard Stitt, Th.M., Ed.D.
Revision Editor:	Alan Christopherson, M.S.

Alpha Omega Publications

a division of:

Bridgestone Multimedia Group

300 North McKemy Avenue, Chandler, Arizona 85226-2618

THE TOOLS OF THE GEOGRAPHER

Geography is the science concerned with the study and description of the ways man adapts to conditions on the earth's surface. As a scientist, the geographer uses special tools to help him in his work. The geographer's tools include the globe, maps, graphs, charts, and a variety of other resource materials. The word *geography* means *to write about the earth.* The tools of the geographer, thus, help him to write about the earth. Geography is neither man-centered nor earth-centered; geography is God-centered. God created the world and has given man the ability to study it. Man's tools are merely "helps" in the exciting discovery of God's wonderful world. In the very beginning of time, God told man to subdue the earth (Genesis 1:28). To subdue or to conquer something, you must learn about it; to learn about something, you must have tools with which to explore it. The Christian studies geography to fulfill his Lord's command given in the garden of Eden. This LIFEPAC will help you to learn about and to use effectively the geographer's tools.

OBJECTIVES

Read these objectives. The objectives tell you what you will be able to do when you have successfully completed this LIFEPAC.

When you have finished this LIFEPAC, you should be able

1. To explain why the globe is the most accurate representation of the earth's surface,
2. To name the four hemispheres of the earth and the lines that divide them,
3. To explain the two uses of an analemma,
4. To measure distances on a map by using a scale of miles,
5. To list the different kinds of maps,
6. To locate a position on a map using latitude and longitude,
7. To state a purpose of graphs and charts,
8. To list the different kinds of graphs,
9. To describe two qualities of an effective chart, and
10. To identify three sources of geographic material found in a library.

Survey the LIFEPAC. Ask yourself some questions about this study. Write your questions here.

_____
_____
_____
_____
_____
_____
_____
_____
_____
_____

I. THE EARTH IN MODEL FORM—THE GLOBE

Many classrooms are equipped with what appears to be a miniature world. Perhaps you have seen this miniature earth flattened into a map or describe statistically on a chart. The most realistic representation of our world is the globe. The globe is a marvelous invention, but it is only an invention. The globe is only a *model* of the real thing, the earth. As you study about the world, as represented by the globe, you will learn of the wisdom and power of a God who loved man enough to create a wonderful world for him. The globe helps to explain what happens in the world simply because the earth is circular. As you consider the invention of the globe, you should understand the explanation for day and night, the explanation for the seasons of the year, the explanation for directional guidance, and the explanation for the forces, such as gravity, you feel acting upon you. How does the globe impress you? The appearance of the earth is breathtaking! As the United States astronauts were returning from the moon in 1969, they exclaimed they were overwhelmed with the sky blue sight of the rising earth. The appearance of the globe helps to explain the curvature of the earth, as well as its tilt, or inclination. Man has arbitrarily divided the globe into parts to help him live on the earth. Looking at a globe helps you to understand man's divisions of latitude lines, longitude lines, time belts, the International Date Line, and the analemma.

SECTION OBJECTIVES

Read these objectives to learn what you should be able to do when you have completed this section.
1. To explain why the globe is the most accurate representation of the earth's surface,
2. To name the four hemispheres of the earth and the lines that divide them, and
3. To explain the two uses of an analemma.

VOCABULARY

Study these words to enhance your learning success in this section.

arbitrary (är´ bu trer ē). Based on one's preference or whim.

axis (ak´ sis). A straight line about which an objects rotates.

distort (di stôrt´). To twist out of shape or misrepresent.

hemisphere (hem´ u sfir). Half of a sphere or globe; any of the halves (northern, southern, eastern, western) of the earth.

revolve (ri volv´). To move in an orbit.

rotate (rō´ tā t). To move or turn around, as a wheel.

sphere (sfir). Any round body; globe; ball.

Note: All vocabulary words in this LIFEPAC appear in **boldface** print the first time they are used. If you are unsure of the meaning when you are reading, study the definitions given.

Pronunciation Key: hat, āge, cāre, fär; let, ēqual, tėrm; it, īce; hot, ōpen, ôrder; oil; out; cup, pu̇t, rüle; child; long; thin; /TH/ for then; /zh/ for measure; /u/ represents /a/ in about, /e/ in taken, /i/ in pencil, /o/ in lemon, and /u/ in circus.

THE INVENTION OF THE GLOBE

The globe is an accurate representation of the world. In fact, the globe is more accurate than any other representation of the earth. The globe helps us to visualize what the world actually looks like. The globe can be used as a valuable guide for travel. The world that the globe represents exerts an influence in the way everyone lives. Certain events occur at certain times in certain ways because man lives on a circular surface. The invention of the globe has been a valuable tool for the geographer.

A picture of the earth today. Pretend to take a trip around the world. If you began walking to the west in a straight line and walked as far as you could go, would you ever arrive back where you started? What would happen if you started walking to the east in a straight line? To make such a trip on foot is impossible, but you can take such a trip on a globe. Put your finger on the globe, spin the globe to the east or west, and see whether your finger arrives where it began. The original location will return under your fingertip because of the circular shape of the earth. The globe represents the circular shape of the earth.

The earth can also be represented on flat maps but not as accurately as on a globe. Flat maps **distort** the true picture of the earth because the earth is a **sphere**; it is not flat. Distances, areas, and directions of round objects are often distorted when they are represented on flat surfaces. An orange can give you a good idea about the difficulties of representing a round object in a flat manner. Suppose that you were able to remove the insides of an orange without disturbing the outer peel. You would then have an object that looked like an orange but with nothing inside. Now suppose you wanted to glue that orange peel to a poster to show your classmates something about oranges. You want to expose every inch of that outer peel on a flat piece of paper. If you flattened the peel, would your end result look like an orange? Perhaps you can understand the difficulty of representing the spherical earth on a flat map. The globe is the most accurate model of the earth's surface.

Because the globe gives a true picture of the location of land and water, it can be used to explain a variety of events that occur on earth. Many years ago the sun was assumed to have **revolved** around the earth. We know now that the earth revolves around the sun. The revolution of the circular earth around the sun accounts for the four seasons of the year. The earth in its orbit varies in its distance from the sun. When the earth is nearer to the sun, the weather is warmer, as in the summer. When the earth is farther from the sun, the weather is cooler, as in the winter. Another factor that accounts for the seasons on earth is the shape of the earth and the tilt of the earth on its **axis**. Because the earth is spherical, the sun's rays are received on an angle and are spread out. The rays that are spread out rather than received directly are not as intense. The tilt of the earth increases the spread over certain areas of the earth and causes these areas to be cooler during certain times of the year.

The earth **rotates** on its axis once every twenty-four hours. When your home is on the side of earth away from the sun, your area will be dark. When your home is toward the sun, your home will be in the daylight hours. The earth takes $365\frac{1}{4}$ of these twenty-four hour days to make one trip around the sun.

The Greeks were the first to use the globe. More than sixteen hundred years before the time of Columbus, scientists were certain that the earth was round rather than flat. These Greek scientists reproduced the earth in the form of a globe in approximately 150 B.C. Of course, much of their work was guesswork. They assumed the existence of many of the countries around the Mediterranean Sea. They believed that the globe had to be balanced; and this belief, ironically, led to their prediction of the existence of the Americas and of Australia.

Although many different types of globes exist, the most common is the political globe. This globe shows the countries of the earth and uses a color scheme to show the various depths of the oceans and heights of the land.

Answer *true* **or** *false*.

1.1	_____	The globe represents the circular shape of the earth.
1.2	_____	The earth's shape is not distorted by a flat map.
1.3	_____	The globe is not the most accurate representation of the earth's surface.
1.4	_____	The earth takes 365¼ days to make one trip around the sun.
1.5	_____	The earth rotates once every twenty-four hours.

Complete these statements.

1.6 The first people to use the globe to represent the earth were the _____ .

1.7 The globe was first produced in the year _____ .

1.8 The early globe predicted the existence of two great continents,
a. _____ and b. _____ .

1.9 The most common type of globe is the _____ globe.

1.10 Depths of oceans and heights of land are represented on certain globes by the use of _____ .

A guide in travel. Most people travel only short distances and, thus, use only a flat map to plan their trip. Although all of the earth's surface is curved, it appears to be flat when we travel only a short distance. When we desire to travel great distances, such as halfway around the world, the globe becomes a better guide for travel than a map. When curved surfaces are represented on flat surfaces, distances are distorted. An example of such distortion occurs when traveling from the continental United States to Hawaii, the fiftieth state. Only two methods of travel to Hawaii are available, by air and by water. To get a true picture of how to get there, the globe would give the most accurate information. Although both a flat map and a globe reveal where Hawaii is located, only a globe does not distort the distance involved.

A knowledge of the globe helps us in our day to day travels. If you travel toward the east in the early morning hours, you will have difficulty seeing because the sun rises in the east. We often talk about the sun rising, but the sun does not really move. The movement of the earth causes differences to exist in the sun's position making it appear to rise.

People who are involved with global travel, such as pilots and navigators, must be well acquainted with the round shape of the earth. A flight from New York to London could become a very long one if routes were planned using a flat map instead of the globe. To plan the shortest trip using a flat map, the plane would leave New York, cross the Atlantic Ocean just south of Newfoundland, and arrive in London. Using the globe to plan the flight, the plane leaves New York, flies directly over Newfoundland, and arrives in London. Which flight is shortest? Although the flat map appears to indicate otherwise, the flight directly over Newfoundland is really shorter. You can see the route differences by stretching a piece of string from New York to London. The string must be curved to the south to follow this route. You will find that you need to use more string when following a path that bypasses Newfoundland. The globe is a valuable aid in understanding world travel.

Write the letter for the correct answer.

1.11 When traveling a short distance, most people use only a _____ to plan their trip.
a. globe
b. light
c. map
d. color scheme

1.12 When curved surfaces are represented on flat surfaces, distances are _____ .
a. forgotten
b. distorted
c. estimated
d. used

1.13 The sun always rises in the _____ .
a. north
b. south
c. west
d. east

1.14 Understanding world travel is greatly aided by the _____ .
a. globe
b. map
c. sun
d. plane

A force in everyday life. Simply knowing that we live on a large globe helps us to understand why things happen as they do on earth. We make adjustments almost unconsciously for living on a circular surface. Have you ever wondered why grapes are more often planted in north-south rows than in east-west rows? Have you ever wondered why poultry houses generally face south in the United States? Have you ever wondered why rooms that face north in an apartment house in Buenos Aires, are more desirable to tenants? Have you ever wondered why students wear white arm bands as safety precautions in Anchorage, Alaska, when going to and from school in the dark? All of these accommodations are made by people living in various places around the world because of the global nature of the earth. Can you find anything that is done in a certain way in your community simply because you live in a special place on the earth's surface? You may have to think carefully and to look diligently because we do so many things without thinking about them. Just ask yourself, "Would we be doing things any differently if we lived on an entirely flat world?"

Answer these questions.

1.15 How many sides would a flat world have?_____

1.16 What are some changes that a flat world would make? _____

_____

_____

5

THE IMPRESSION OF THE GLOBE

The globe is a model of the earth. When you examine a globe, you may discover that it was not as round as you thought. You may discover that the model does not stand as erect as you thought, but is, instead, tilted as it revolves and rotates. Rather than studying the model as a whole, you may decide to break the model into halves to learn more about it. Finally, you may want to learn how you could represent the model to someone else who is not able to view the model.

The shape of the earth. The earth is a huge sphere, having more water surface than land surface. At the top of the globe in the northernmost position is the North Pole; it is on water. At the bottom of the globe in the southernmost position is the South Pole; it is on land. Contrary to appearances, the earth is not perfectly round. Pictures from the orbiting Vanguard satellite show that the earth is not a round sphere slightly flattened at the poles. Instead, the Vanguard showed that the earth is pear-shaped. The earth bulges almost fifty feet in depth at the South Pole. The earth is, therefore, a slightly pear-shaped sphere. However, these variations are so slight as to be almost unnoticeable. The variations are only fifty feet each over a north-south diameter of the earth of about seven thousand, nine hundred miles!

Write *true* **or** *false*.

1.17	_____	The globe is not a model of the earth.
1.18	_____	The earth has more land surface than water surface.
1.19	_____	The North Pole in on water.
1.20	_____	The earth is slightly pear-shaped.
1.21	_____	The South Pole is on water.
1.22	_____	The Vanguard is an orbiting satellite of the earth.
1.23	_____	The earth is flattened at both poles.
1.24	_____	The north-south diameter of the earth measures only 7,900 feet.
1.25	_____	The earth has never been photographed from outer space.

The position of the earth. Perhaps you have noticed that a globe is never straight up and down, but is always in a tilted, or slanted, position. The **axis** of the earth is also tilted in the same position and always points toward the north. If the earth did not tilt on its axis, the days and nights would be equally long throughout the year everywhere on the earth. This condition would change some of the ways in which we live. Tilting and rotation of the earth (spinning on its axis, always from west to east) determine the different amounts of daylight present in various areas of the world. Tilting and revolution of the earth (orbiting around the sun) determine the seasonal changes that occur in the world.

Follow these directions and answer this question. Put a check in the box when each step is completed.

☐   Make three columns on a sheet of paper, and head the columns "Date," "Time of Sunrise," and "Time of Sunset."

☐   Determine how many hours of sunshine your city enjoys each day by finding the difference between the time of sunrise and the time of sunset. The hours of sunrise and sunset should be listed in your daily paper.

☐   Find a weekly average of the number of sunshine hours by totaling the number of daylight hours in a week and then dividing by the number of days in the week.

☐   Maintain your record for four weeks.

1.26   Did the average number of daylight hours per week increase or decrease over the four-week period? _____

_____

Complete these statements.

1.27   The earth always rotates from a. _____ to b. _____ .

1.28   When the earth rotates, it spins on its _____ .

1.29   The earth revolves by orbiting around the _____ .

1.30   Seasonal changes are determined by a. _____ and b. _____ .

The halves of the earth. Man has drawn an imaginary line around the earth that divides it into two equal parts—a northern part and a southern part. This imaginary line is the equator. The equator is midway between the North Pole and the South Pole. Each half of the earth is a **hemisphere**. The earth is divided into four hemispheres—northern, southern, western, and eastern. The equator divides the Northern Hemisphere from the Southern Hemisphere, and another imaginary line runs from pole to pole and divides the Western Hemisphere from the Eastern Hemisphere. Because the earth is one sphere, to divide it equally produces two half-spheres, or hemispheres.

What is life like in the Northern Hemisphere, the Southern Hemisphere, or on the equator? For lands near the equator the sun is almost directly overhead at noon, and days and nights are nearly equal in length. As you move from the equator into the Northern Hemisphere between the Tropic of Cancer and the Arctic Circle, the noontime sun appears in the southern sky. In the Northern Hemisphere a definite difference exists between the winter

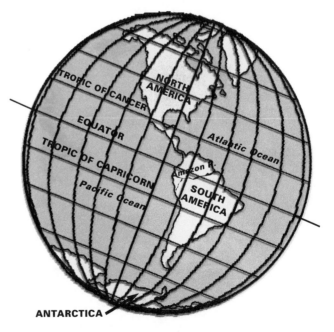

NORTHERN HEMISPHERE

SOUTHERN HEMISPHERE

and the summer seasons. The summer occurs in June, July, and August. As you move from the equator into the Southern Hemisphere, the noontime sun appears in the northern sky. In this area between the Tropic of Capricorn and the Antarctic Circle, a winter and a summer season also occur. However, summer in the Southern Hemisphere occurs during December, January, and February. Although great differences exist between the Northern Hemisphere and the Southern Hemisphere, some similarities also exist. Because the equator receives the sun's rays most directly, it tends to be extremely warm. When you travel away from the area surrounding the equator, whether north or south, you will find cooler regions.

Write the letter of the correct answer in the blank.

1.31   The line that divides the earth into a Northern Hemisphere and a Southern Hemisphere is the _____ .
a. equator   c. midway
b. circle   d. half-line

1.32   The earth has _____ hemispheres.
a. 2   c. 4
b. 0   d. 3

1.33   The line dividing the earth in half is _____ .
a. real   c. thick
b. imaginary   d. blue

1.34   Another term for half-sphere is _____ .
a. equator   c. pole
b. midway   d. hemisphere

1.35   The Northern Hemisphere and the Southern Hemisphere are _____ in size.
a. unequal   c. gaining
b. equal   d. decreasing

Write *true* **or** *false.*

1.36   _____   The sun is nearly directly overhead at noon at the equator.
1.37   _____   No similarities exist between the Northern Hemisphere and the Southern Hemisphere.
1.38   _____   Summer in the Southern Hemisphere occurs in December, January and February.
1.39   _____   The Tropic of Capricorn is in the Southern Hemisphere.
1.40   _____   No summer season occurs in the Northern Hemisphere.
1.41   _____   Days and nights are of equal length at the equator.
1.42   _____   The Tropic of Cancer is in the Northern Hemisphere.
1.43   _____   The Antarctic Circle is in the Northern Hemisphere.
1.44   _____   The Arctic Circle is in the Southern Hemisphere.

The representation of the earth. The globe is the best and most accurate representation of the surface of the earth. Sometimes all of the earth must be represented on the flat surface of a map. Whenever the earth's curved surface is represented on a flat map, distortion occurs. The map may distort true directions, distances, or sizes of land masses. Attempting to correct one type of distortion only creates another. Map projections of the earth's surface are used to fulfill an intended purpose of the map and not to accurately represent the earth in every detail. A projection is a method that transfers portions of the globe to a flat map.

One of the most common maps of the earth's surface is the Mercator projection. This projection shows the surface of the earth on a rectangular map. This map is useful because a line drawn between any two points shows the correct compass direction between the points. Navigators find this feature especially helpful. The greatest disadvantage of this projection is that areas far from the equator are badly distorted and appear much larger than they actually are.

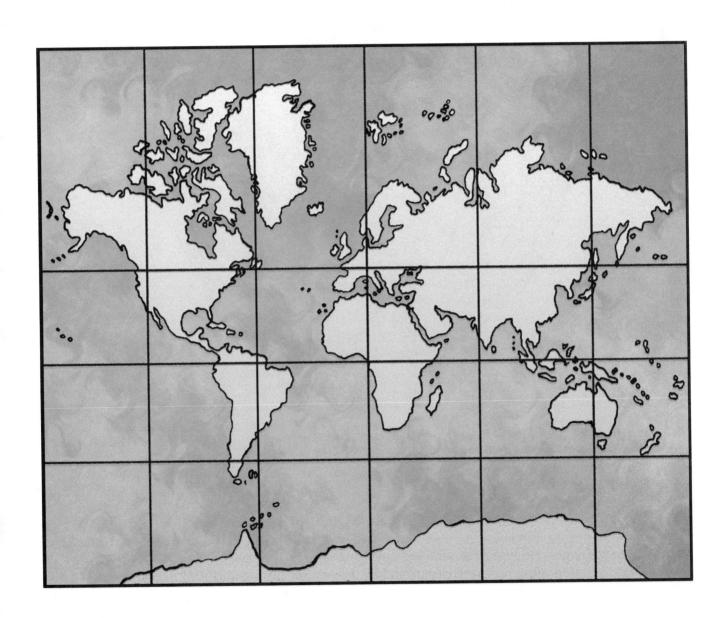

Mercator Projection

An important tool for calculating the distance from one point on the earth's surface to another by air is the azimuthal equidistant projection map. When the North Pole or the South Pole is placed at the center of this map, it is then referred to as a polar projection. Sometimes this projection is called an "air-age map." Any point of the earth's surface can be chosen as the center of this map. Air distances are calculated by measuring the distance from the center of the map to any other point on the map. Lands close to the center of this projection are shown in true size and shape. Air routes use this type of map because routes are indicated more accurately than on other maps. As with other maps, distortion is also this map's greatest disadvantage. The size and shape of land masses becomes more distorted the farther they are located from the center of focus.

AZIMUTHAL EQUIDISTANT PROJECTION

The azimuthal equidistant projection has been greatly used by jet-age navigators. A straight line connecting the center of the map with any other point becomes part of a great-circle route around the world. The straight line will give the exact distance to that point. A great-circle route is the shortest and most direct route between any two points on the earth's surface. The drawing of a great-circle route divides the earth into two equal parts. The equator is an example of a great circle around the earth. Great-circle routes have been used by ships for many years, but airplanes make more extensive use of the routes. Unlike ships, planes can fly over any of earth's obstacles, thus following the great circle. However, current political boundaries may prevent planes from taking the shortest possible route. Air rights are required to fly over certain foreign countries and are sometimes difficult to obtain. A great-circle route can be seen by taking a string and stretching it around the globe. The string divides the globe into two equal parts. If the string were uniformly marked, it could be used to show mileages between points along a great-circle route.

Another important projection of the earth is the interrupted-area projection. To prevent distortion of the continents, blank areas are inserted in the map. These interruptions in the map are usually made in the water surface of the earth. This type or map allows areas to be studied with little distortion. This projection is also useful for showing characteristics of regions. Such characteristics could include natural resources, population, and distributions.

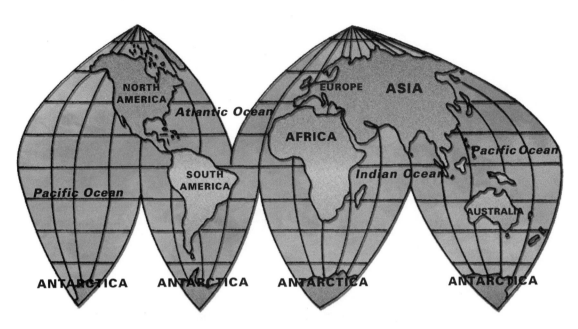

INTERRUPTED-AREA PROJECTION

Complete these statements.

1.45   When the earth's curved surface is represented on a flat surface, such as a map, _____ occurs.

1.46   A method that transfers portions of the globe to a flat map is a _____ .

1.47   The map that shows the earth's surface on a rectangular presentation is the _____ projection.

1.48   A map helpful in charting great-circle routes is the _____ .

1.49   An example of a great circle around the earth is the _____ .

1.50   A great circle divides the earth into _____ equal parts.

1.51   A map that prevents the distortion of continents by inserting interruptions is the

_____ .

Write the letter of the correct answer in the blank.

1.52   Attempting to correct one distortion on a map serves to _____ another.
   a. solve
   b. hide
   c. destroy
   d. create

1.53   Great-circle routes have been used by _____ for years.
- a. ships
- b. camel trains
- c. kites
- d. trains

1.54   To fly over some foreign countries, _____ are required.
- a. passports
- b. credit references
- c. air rights
- d. visas

Complete this activity.

1.55   Using a globe and a piece of string, locate the great circle that goes through your city and Addis Abba, Ethiopia. Write the names of two other cities located on that great circle but not located in the United States.

Teacher check _____

                                  Initial   Date

THE INSTRUCTION OF THE GLOBE

The study of the globe is a lifelong process; you will never finish learning about the globe. You can be instructed about certain aspects of the globe and then begin to build upon these fundamental concepts. One important skill to learn is the use of latitude and longitude to locate a certain position on the globe. The two lines are the only means available to communicate an exact position on the earth's surface. To more fully understand the world in which we live, we must become aware of time belts that span the globe and of the International Date Line.

The world is rapidly becoming a smaller place in which to live. Jet travel allows us to step from one continent to another in the afternoon. Space travelers orbiting the earth can see every country in the world in about the same amount of time that most of us take to eat lunch. Unless we are aware of what is involved in becoming a world traveler, we shall never be at home on our own planet. Did you know, for instance, that in the course of world travels you could live the same day twice? Did you know that you could skip an entire day while traveling, never living one moment of it?

The globe is a unit of instruction all by itself. You can become skillful in the use of the globe by learning to read and use the symbols printed on it. One such helpful tool is the analemma, found on every physical-political classroom globe. Let the globe become your guide to learning more about the wonderful world in which we live.

Latitude and longitude. You can locate any point on the earth's surface by the use of lines of latitude and longitude. The earth was **arbitrarily** divided by man with these lines just as a city is divided by streets and avenues.

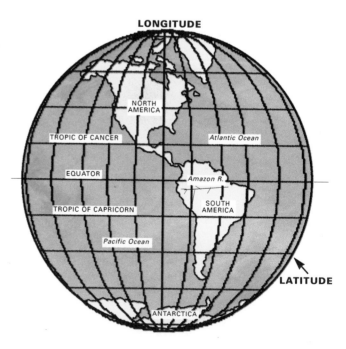

Latitude lines are sometimes called parallels because they are parallel to the equator and to each other. Longitude lines are often referred to as meridians. Lines of longitude extend from the North Pole to the South Pole, and they meet as they approach the poles. Because lines of latitude run the same way as the equator, they are measured in degrees north or south of the equator. The equator is 0 (zero) degrees latitude, and both poles are 90 degrees. Longitude lines are measured in degrees in terms of being east or west of the prime meridian. The prime meridian is the first meridian that was arbitrarily established by man. Scientists determined that the first, or prime, meridian would pass through Greenwich, England. Greenwich is, therefore, listed as 0 degrees longitude.

Any feature or location on the earth's surface can easily be described in terms of latitude and longitude. Lines of latitude allow the location to be described as being either north or south of the equator, and lines of longitude reveal how far east or west the location is from the prime meridian.

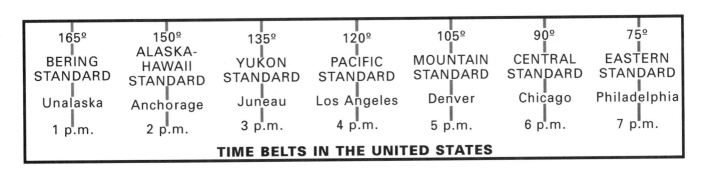

165°	150°	135°	120°	105°	90°	75°
BERING STANDARD	ALASKA-HAWAII STANDARD	YUKON STANDARD	PACIFIC STANDARD	MOUNTAIN STANDARD	CENTRAL STANDARD	EASTERN STANDARD
Unalaska	Anchorage	Juneau	Los Angeles	Denver	Chicago	Philadelphia
1 p.m.	2 p.m.	3 p.m.	4 p.m.	5 p.m.	6 p.m.	7 p.m.

TIME BELTS IN THE UNITED STATES

Time belts. Before 1883 the United States and Canada used fifty-three different time systems. With the invention of more rapid means of travel, such as the train, something had to be done to make time systems more uniform. The United States was divided into four time zones, and Canada was divided into five zones. The entire earth is divided into twenty-four time belts, or zones. Each zone is 15 degrees of longitude wide. (A circle contains 360 degrees; 360 degrees divided by twenty-four time belts equals 15 degrees for each belt.)

The time changes by one hour each 15 degrees of longitude you travel to the east or to the west. To avoid splitting cities or states into two time belts, the boundaries of the time zones were made slightly irregular. Therefore, the time in the time belt just west of where you are now, is always an hour earlier, and the time in the time belt to the east is an hour later. The United States used to have only four time zones; but, with the admission of Alaska and Hawaii, the United States now extends through seven time zones. Those seven zones include *Eastern, Central, Mountain, Pacific, Yukon, Alaska,* and *Bering.* A six-hour difference exists between the easternmost city in the United States (Eastern Standard Time) and the westernmost city in the United States (Bering Standard Time).

 Complete these statements.

1.56   Before 1883 the United States and Canada had _____ time belts.

1.57   Each time zone around the world is _____ degrees of longitude wide.

1.58   The United States extends through _____ time belts.

1.59   You can locate any point on the earth's surface by the use of lines of
         a. _____ and b. _____ .

1.60   Before the admission of Alaska and Hawaii, the United States extended through
         _____ time zones.

International Date Line. The earth is divided into twenty-four time zones, each zone one hour different from the zone on either side of it.. As the time zones spread to the east and the west away from the Prime Meridian, they meet exactly halfway around the world at the 180th meridian (180 degrees east or west longitude). This line where the time belts meet is the International Date Line. By crossing the International Date Line to the west you gain, or add, one day (all twenty-four time zones). By crossing the International Date Line to the east you lose, or subtract, one day (all twenty-four time zones). When the time is noon on Saturday of June 1 on the east side of the International Date Line, the time is noon on Sunday of June 2 on the west side of the line. Suppose you were on a ship that left the West Coast of the United States, heading for the Orient. You are traveling straight west and the date is Friday, May 31. You can hardly wait until tomorrow because your birthday is June 1. During the night while you are sleeping, the ship crosses the International Date Line. When you awaken in the morning, you discover that the date is now Sunday, June 2! The day Saturday, your birthday, was skipped, or lost. On your return trip to the United States, you will gain back the day you lost. The International Date Line does not follow exactly the 180th meridian. By agreement the line has been made somewhat irregular to help cities and countries through which the 180th meridian passes. Much confusion would result from having two separate dates existing at the same time on one island! For this reason the International Date Line has been moved to the east or west of places to avoid dividing communities into two different days.

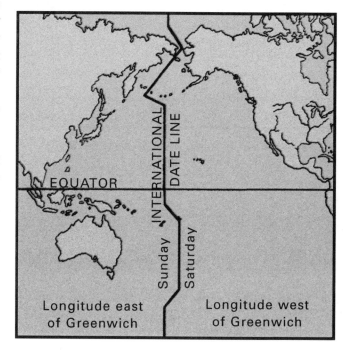

International Date Line

![sphere icon] **Write** *true* **or** *false.*

1.61 _____ The earth is divided into twenty-four time zones.

1.62 _____ Each time zone is two hours wide.

1.63 _____ You lose a day when you cross the International Date Line traveling west.

1.64 _____ The International Date Line follows exactly the 180th meridian.

The analemma. When studying the globe, perhaps you have noticed the device that looks like a figure eight in the east central Pacific Ocean. It is called the analemma, meaning *sundial*. It is a very precise instrument that shows two facts. One, it shows the latitude at which the sun will be directly overhead at noon on specific dates. Two, it shows the difference between man's clock time and sun time. This difference is called the equation of time.

Between the Tropic of Cancer and the Tropic of Capricorn, the sun's rays shine directly down at noon on any particular spot during two days of the year. The analemma helps you to determine what those two days are for any latitude between the Tropic of Cancer and the

Tropic of Capricorn. If you want to find those two days for a particular location, follow the location's parallel to the analemma. Where the parallel intersects, the analemma gives those dates when the sun's rays will be directly overhead.

The scale in the center of the analemma is used to compute the difference between sun time and clock time. A solar day is measured from the sun noon of one day to the sun noon of another day. If we measured our days by solar day measurement, very few days would be of the same length. Man measures his days by clock time so that all the days are uniform in length. The analemma can help you to find the difference on any given day between these two means of measuring time. First, find the day you are interested in on the analemma. With a piece of paper, measure the distance from the day perpendicular to the axis running through the center of the analemma. After marking these points, lay them on the time scale that crosses the analemma. Counting the minutes between the two points will reveal the difference in minutes between the solar time and the clock time. The clock is slow if the date falls to the right of the axis. The clock is fast if the date falls to the left of the axis.

God has promised (Revelation 21:1) that He would provide ". . . a new heaven and a new earth. . . ." As Christians we are excited about the future, for we know that God is in control of everything. Someday even time as we know it will pass away, and we shall experience the reality of II Peter 3:8, ". . . One day is with the Lord as a thousand years, and a thousand years as one day." We must be faithful to be instructed in His world of today so that we shall be able to praise Him during all eternity for the wonderful world He created. Our praise will then be multiplied as our Father in heaven continues to make great things even greater!

The Analemma

Answer these questions.

1.65   What two things does the analemma show?

a. _____

b. _____

1.66   What is the difference between sun time and clock time for March 26? _____

1.67   Is the clock fast or slow for March 26? _____

Teacher check _____

                                            Initial   Date

Review the material in this section in preparation for the Self Test. The Self Test will check your mastery of this particular section. The items missed on this Self Test will indicate specific areas where restudy is needed for mastery.

SELF TEST 1

Complete these statements (each answer, 3 points).

1.01   The earth rotates once every _____ .

1.02   The most accurate representation of the earth's surface is the _____ .

1.03   The first people to use the globe were the _____ .

1.04   The four hemispheres of earth are the a. _____ , b. _____ ,
              c. _____ , and d. _____ .

1.05   The earth always rotates from a. _____ to b. _____ .

1.06   Three types of global maps are the a. _____ , b. _____ ,
              and c. _____ .

1.07   Two lines that help locate any position on the earth's surface are
              a. _____ and b. _____ .

1.08   The original four time zones of the United States, from east to west are
              a. _____ , b. _____ , c. _____ , and
              d. _____ .

Match these items (each answer, 2 points).

1.09 _____ axis   a. orbit

1.010 _____ hemisphere   b. distort

1.011 _____ equator   c. great circle

1.012 _____ revolution   d. rotate

1.013 _____ 180th meridian   e. half of earth

1.014 _____ analemma   f. International Date Line

1.015 _____ prime   g. globe

1.016 _____ sphere   h. sun time

1.017 _____ map   i. 0 degrees

1.018 _____ Vanguard   j. distract

                                                          k. satellite

Write *true* **or** *false* (each answer, 1 point).

1.019 _____ The earth is not straight but tilted.

1.020 _____ The equator is a real, not an imaginary line.

1.021 _____ Great-circle routes are no longer used for travel.

1.022 _____ A time belt, or zone, is 15 degrees of longitude wide.

1.023 _____ The earth is divided into thirty-three time zones.

1.024 _____ The International Date Line is not longer used.

1.025 _____ The analemma is used to determine how far a country is located from the equator.

Write the letter for the correct answer (each answer, 2 points).

1.026 The north-south diameter of the earth is _____ .

    a. 9,700 miles

    b. 7,900 miles

    c. 180 miles

    d. 360 degrees

1.027 Tilting and revolution determine the earth's _____ .

    a. meridians

    b. axis

    c. shape

    d. seasons

1.028 When curved surfaces are represented on flat surfaces, distances are _____ .

    a. shortened

    b. lengthened

    c. distorted

    d. unchanged

1.029 A method that transfers portions of the globe to a flat map is _____ .

    a. impossible

    b. curving

    c. a dilemma

    d. a projection

1.030 The earth revolves once every _____ .

    a. $365\frac{1}{4}$ days

    b. twenty-four hours

    c. 180 degrees

    d. season

Answer this question (each part, 5 points).

1.031 What two things does the analemma show?

    a. _____

    _____

    b. _____

    _____

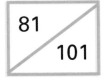

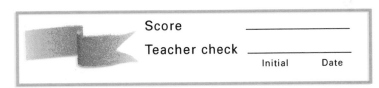

Score _____

Teacher check _____

               Initial   Date

II. THE EARTH IN PICTURE FORM — THE MAP

Maps are essential tools of the geographer. Maps reduce the world to a size and a shape that man can readily study. Maps continue to be refined over the years as man's knowledge of geographical features increases. Maps give meaning to the wide range of details which fill your life. Major news broadcasts rely on maps to explain what is happening in the world today. By the use of a map, we gain greater understanding of places and relationships. The individual who is not able to properly read or interpret maps will find himself at a disadvantage in today's world.

Many different kinds of maps are made. Each kind of map is suited to a particular purpose. In this section several different kinds of maps will be presented. The uses of maps and the ways you can make maps, will also be discussed.

God has given man a "map" to help guide him through life. In fact, this map has been designed by God to lead man to life eternal. Maps give us a knowledge of which way to go. David, the Psalmist, said of God's map (Psalm 119:105), "Thy word is a lamp unto my feet and a light unto my path." God's map for your life is the Bible, and it can give "light unto your path." To benefit from the Bible, just like a map, you must be able to read it and interpret it. Jesus has given Christians His Holy Spirit to help them apply His Word to their lives. Make God's Word, the Bible, your map of life!

SECTION OBJECTIVES

Read these objectives to learn what you should be able to do when you have completed this section.

4.   To measure distances on a map by using a scale of miles,
5.   To list the different kinds of maps, and
6.   To locate a position on a map using latitude and longitude.

VOCABULARY

Study these words to enhance your learning success in this section.

abstract (ab strakt´). Thought of apart from material objects; the opposite of concrete.
circumference (sur kum´ fur uns). The distance around a circle or other rounded surface.
data (dā´ tu). Facts from which conclusions can be drawn.
legend (lej´ und). A title or key accompanying an illustration or map.
topographic (top u graf´ ik). Relating to the surface of an area or a detailed description or drawing of that area.

READING AND INTERPRETING MAPS

Maps are fundamental to geography. Being able to use an important tool, such as a map, is crucial. Using a map requires the ability to read and interpret the map's symbols, features, and scale of distances. Practice is an important part of learning to read and interpret a map. Maps provide a way to visualize a landscape without actually being there or seeing a photograph. Maps reveal relationships of geographical conditions and man's activities. The use of maps can become a lifelong and enjoyable practice if time is taken to learn to read and interpret map symbols and scales skillfully. A difference exists between reading and interpreting maps. Reading is what we do when we study a map to find a particular location. We read a map solely to obtain information from it. Interpretation is what takes place after the map is read. Interpreting the **data** we gather from map reading involves making inferences and drawing conclusions. In reading a map, you merely have to be able to read the symbols; in interpreting a map, you must be able to read "between the lines." You must discover the meaning that lies behind the map's symbols. You will know that you are successful in reading and interpreting maps when you are able to visualize what a map seeks to portray, to make inferences and draw conclusions from a map's information, to see relationships from a map, to freely refer to maps for personal help, and to construct your own maps when the need arises.

➡️ **Write the correct answer in each blank.**

2.1 Using a map requires the ability to _____ .
    a. pick and choose
    b. read and interpret
    c. draw and measure
    d. trace and sketch

2.2 Reading "between the lines" of a map has to do with _____ .
    a. reading
    b. representing
    c. interpreting
    d. scaling

2.3 To find a particular location, we _____ a map.
    a. read
    b. ignore
    c. interpret
    d. symbolize

2.4 Maps are fundamental to the science of _____ .
    a. biology
    b. mathematics
    c. geology
    d. geography

2.5 Maps help us to _____ a landscape.
    a. forget
    b. prepare
    c. visualize
    d. ignore

2.6 The ability to construct your own map indicates _____ .
    a. success
    b. failure
    c. confusion
    d. forgetfulness

Map symbols. Maps possess their own special language. The map's language, or symbols, are related to actual geographic features. To visualize what the map is communicating, you must master the language of symbols. Symbols are **abstract**. Sometimes an area is difficult to visualize by merely reading the map symbols. The ability to visualize must be developed and practiced.

The symbols that a map uses are explained in the **legend** of the map. The symbols are matched with the verbal picture it represents. An example of this matching is found in Figure 1.

SYMBOL	FEATURE DEPICTED
Blue	Water
Green	Lowland Elevations
Brown	Mountains
White	Glaciers - Snow
	Mountain
 ~~~	River
— · — · — · —	National boundary

Figure 1

Follow these directions and answer the questions. Put a check in the box when each step is completed.

> **These supplies are needed:**
> sand (or dirt)
> cake pan (approximately 9 inches by 15 inches)

☐ 1. Fill the pan three-fourths full of sand (or dirt).

☐ 2. Add as much sand (or dirt) as necessary to the pan to make a landscape that includes rivers and tributaries, mountains, peninsulas, and valleys.

☐ 3. Draw your landscape on a sheet of paper, using symbols rather than pictures to show your land features.

☐ 4. Explain what your symbols represent in a key (a small box) at the bottom of your map.

2.7 What symbol did you use to indicate mountains?

_____

2.8 Why is representing a three-dimensional landscape on two-dimensional paper difficult?

_____

_____

 Write *true* or *false*.

2.9 _____ Most maps do not rely on the use of symbols.

2.10 _____ The map's key explains its symbols.

2.11 _____ Map symbols are generally unrelated to actual geographical features.

2.12 _____ Symbols are often difficult to understand because they are abstract.

Map scale of miles. Another important feature of every good map is a scale of miles. To represent a large area of geography on a small paper surface, the map must be scaled down. The scale of miles is usually found at the bottom of a map.

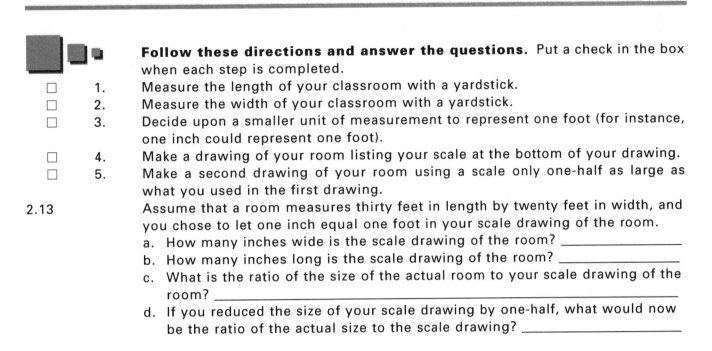

Follow these directions and answer the questions. Put a check in the box when each step is completed.

☐ 1. Measure the length of your classroom with a yardstick.

☐ 2. Measure the width of your classroom with a yardstick.

☐ 3. Decide upon a smaller unit of measurement to represent one foot (for instance, one inch could represent one foot).

☐ 4. Make a drawing of your room listing your scale at the bottom of your drawing.

☐ 5. Make a second drawing of your room using a scale only one-half as large as what you used in the first drawing.

2.13 Assume that a room measures thirty feet in length by twenty feet in width, and you chose to let one inch equal one foot in your scale drawing of the room.

a. How many inches wide is the scale drawing of the room? _____

b. How many inches long is the scale drawing of the room? _____

c. What is the ratio of the size of the actual room to your scale drawing of the room? _____

d. If you reduced the size of your scale drawing by one-half, what would now be the ratio of the actual size to the scale drawing? _____

Mapmakers sometimes allow an inch to represent several hundred miles. This scaling down allows the mapmaker to represent large areas on a small space. Scales of miles will vary from map to map because many maps are of different sizes.

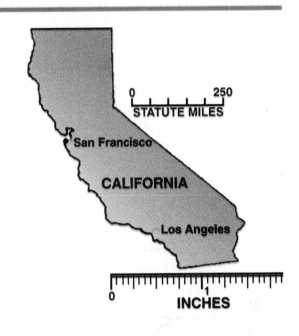

Figure 2

Complete these statements. Refer to Figure 2.

2.14 On the scale of miles, one inch equals _____ miles.

2.15 The distance between the two towns is approximately _____ miles.

21

TYPES OF MAPS

Hundreds of varieties of maps exist today. No one type of map is best. Different kinds of maps are suited to different purposes. Maps in most classrooms show distributions and locations of cities within political boundaries. A map well-suited to the purposes of teaching geography is one that includes related cultural and environmental aspects. Such a map is called physical-political. While studying this section of the LIFEPAC, examine the various maps found in your classroom and home. Try to determine how many different kinds of maps are represented in your school and home. A local library could help in your search for more varieties of maps.

Distribution maps. Most classrooms have distribution maps. These maps are made in two different styles: one uses shading in various colors and the other uses dots. The colors or dots are used to indicate higher or lower concentrations of whatever is being measured. Distribution maps may show rainfall, crops, population, or a variety of other things present in certain areas of a country. Through the use of these maps, one geographic area can easily be compared to another in terms of distribution.

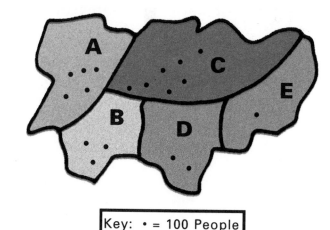

Key: • = 100 People

Figure 3

Answer these questions.

2.16 How many people does one dot represent? _____

2.17 How many people live in state C? _____

2.18 Which state has the lowest population? _____

2.19 Assuming each dot represented 10,000 people, what would be the population of state B? _____

Complete this activity and answer the questions.

2.20 Fill in the distribution map using the figures given.

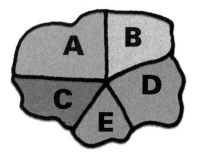

state A	2,900,000
state B	700,000
state C	2,300,000
state D	3,200,000
state E	600,000

Key: 1 dot = 100,000 people

2.21 How many dots did you place in state C? _____

2.22 Which state had the least number of dots? _____

HISTORY & GEOGRAPHY

909

LIFEPAC TEST

79 / 99

Name _____

Date _____

Score _____

HISTORY & GEOGRAPHY 909: LIFEPAC TEST

Match these items (each answer, 2 points).

1. _____ bar graph
2. _____ relief map
3. _____ pictograph
4. _____ outline map
5. _____ broken bar graph
6. _____ sketch map
7. _____ distribution map
8. _____ road map
9. _____ circle graph
10. _____ line graph
11. _____ topographic map
12. _____ pictorial map

a. symbols
b. most accurate
c. highways
d. numbers
e. decorative
f. refines pictograph
g. contour lines
h. three-dimensional
i. relationship
j. 100 per cent
k. geographical shape
l. refines broken bar graph
m. quick

Write *true* **or** *false* (each answer, 1 point).

13. _____ The Prime Meridian is a great circle.
14. _____ The equator divides the Northern Hemisphere from the Southern Hemisphere.
15. _____ A time belt is equivalent to one hour.
16. _____ Some outline maps use population dots.
17. _____ Mercator projection maps are used to determine great-circle routes.
18. _____ A graph is often used for comparison.
19. _____ A purpose of a chart is to organize information.
20. _____ The earth is most accurately represented by a globe.
21. _____ An effective chart helps to clarify understanding.
22. _____ The analemma is located north of the Tropic of Cancer.

Complete these statements (each answer, 3 points).

23. When curved surfaces are portrayed on a flat surface, distances are _____ .

24. A method that transfers portions of a globe to a flat map is a _____ .

25. The most commonly used source of geographical material is an _____ .

26. A book of maps is called an _____ .

27. The South American Handbook is a geographical reference work found in a _____ .

28. The type of line separating the Eastern Hemisphere and the Western Hemisphere is called a _____ .

29. The type of line separating the Northern Hemisphere and the Southern Hemisphere is called a _____ .

30. The symbols of a map are explained in its _____.
31. The earth rotates once every _____.
32. The earth revolves once every _____.
33. Two lines that help locate any point on the earth's surface are
    a. _____ and b. _____.

Write the letter of the correct answer in the blank (each answer, 2 points).

34. Graphs and charts are forms of _____ aid.
    a. audio
    b. internal
    c. visual
    d. financial

35. Another name for a line graph is a _____ graph.
    a. trend
    b. pie
    c. slope
    d. flow

36. To determine _____ on a map you would use a scale of miles.
    a. elevations
    b. distances
    c. landforms
    d. populations

37. The truest representation of the earth is the _____.
    a. Mercator projection map
    b. azimuthal equidistant projection map
    c. interrupted-area projection map
    d. distribution map

38. What determines the most appropriate graph is the type of_____ needed.
    a. symbol
    b. information
    c. comparison
    d. summary

39. The equator is not _____.
    a. a great circle
    b. a meridian
    c. a parallel
    d. 0 degrees

40. The analemma shows _____.
    a. distance
    b. rotation
    c. longitude
    d. sun time

Answer these questions (each answer, 5 points).

41. What does the analemma show with respect to latitude?

_____

_____

2

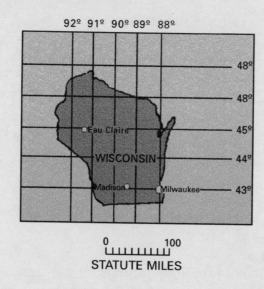

0 — 100
STATUTE MILES

42.   What is the location of Milwaukee in terms of latitude and longitude?
_____

43.   What is the distance from Madison to Eau Claire? _____

NOTES

Write *true* **or** *false.*

2.23 _____ The two states with the greatest population distribution are states A and C.

2.24 _____ The combines population distributions of states A and B is greater than that of states C and E.

2.25 _____ A distribution map immediately reveals areas of higher concentrations.

2.26 _____ Distribution maps do not reveal areas of low concentrations.

Although a wide variety of distribution maps exists, they all possess common features. When making your own distribution map, remember to include elements that will make your map excellent. The map should have a title that is meaningful. On the map show only the one thing that is mentioned in the title. If one map tries to show too many things, it becomes confusing to the reader and hard to use as a geographical tool. The map should be of the same size and color. All maps need a key that will unlock the door of understanding for the reader. Including a scale of miles often makes a map more meaningful. Finding or drawing good distribution maps is not always easy, but serious readers will appreciate the effort.

Outline maps. Outline maps are the most common of all types of maps used in the classroom. An outline map is geographically accurate but gives only an outline of the area being studied. The student must fill in the map with important details. Although the outline map does not give many details, it does give a general geographic description. Such a general description can often be valuable in learning to recognize an area.

Figure 4

2.27   Which state appear to be the largest? _____

2.28   Which state is a peninsula? _____

2.29   Do the states appear generally to be geographically larger in the western or eastern half of the country? _____

2.30   How many states border the Pacific Ocean? _____

Write *true* **or** *false.*

2.31   _____   Outline maps are not commonly used.

2.32   _____   An outline map is useful because it contains the names of all geographic features.

2.33   _____   An outline map is geographically accurate.

2.34   _____   An outline map contains nothing more than a geographic outline.

Sketch maps. A sketch map is just what its title implies, a sketch. Sketch maps are drawn freehand and usually are drawn very quickly. They serve the purpose of presenting geographic facts and relationships. This quick presentation is generally clear although not precisely accurate. Sketch maps are used mainly to illustrate an immediate point, such as in a discussion. Once the map's use has been completed, it is usually discarded. You may often have used a sketch map when describing a certain area to a friend or giving a talk in front of the class. The map greatly illustrates what you are verbally explaining.

Complete this activity.

2.35   Make a sketch map of your home in relation to your school. Include major streets and compass directions.

Answer these questions.

2.36   Why are sketch maps not precisely accurate?

_____

_____

2.37   Name some situations in which sketch maps could prove very helpful.

_____

_____

_____

_____

_____

Pictorial maps. Maps are sometimes designed to be more decorative than geographically accurate. Such is the case with the pictorial map. A pictorial map shows the symbol of a product that is present in a certain area of a country. An example of a pictorial map would be a corn stalk drawn on the state of Nebraska or a cactus drawn on the state of Arizona. Pictorial maps must be studied and used with care, for they can lead to serious misconceptions. For instance, someone could assume that nothing but corn grows in Nebraska and nothing but cactuses grow in Arizona. Often a symbol is printed in a size that is not proportionate to the country or state.

Although pictorial maps have these limitations, they serve a valuable purpose by illustrating major products of an area.

Road maps. A common map used in everyday life is the road map. To understand a road, or route map, the symbols of the map must be carefully studied. The lack of a careful study of map symbols has often led to confusion on the highways among adult drivers. To further your understanding, find a road map of your state. Take an imaginary trip across your state selecting which routes you will take and computing your mileage between major towns and cities.

► ► ► **Answer these questions.**

2.38   What are three major interstate highways that cross the state in which you live?

2.39   Select a major highway and compute the number of miles it covers in crossing your state.

_____

_____

2.40   Why are many adults confused by a road map? _____

_____

Relief maps. A map is a drawing of the earth's surface. Miguel de Cervantes said, "Journey over all the universe in a map." Some maps make this journey appear more realistic than other maps. One such lifelike map is the relief map. Through the use of a relief map you can become familiar with a region's size, shape, boundaries, and geographic features. Mountains, valleys, rivers, lakes, and elevations are all made more real through the use of a relief map. A relief map differs from most other maps in that it is three-dimensional. A three-dimensional map has a raised surface which shows the physical features of a mapped area. Relief maps are not only easy to read, but are easier to interpret than two-dimensional maps that use only symbols. By looking at a relief map, you immediately realize that the earth has an uneven surface; you then are able to interpret results from your map reading. For instance, the easy reading of the relief map may help you to understand climactic conditions resulting from different elevations. The knowledge of climactic conditions may then help you to interpret what crops are grown, what clothing is worn, and what is the amount of annual rainfall.

Follow these directions and answer the question. Put a check in the box when each step is completed.

These supplies are needed:
    one piece of cardboard (9 inches by 12 inches)
    a stapler
    outline maps ($8\frac{1}{2}$ inches by 11 inches)
    transparent plastic bags (at least 10 inches by 13 inches)
    transparent tape
    salt
    flour
    water
    mixing bowls
    tempera paints and brushes
    black tape

☐   1.   Make and $8\frac{1}{2}$ by 11 inch outline map of a state, county, or region. (Note: Use a physical-political map, found in a text or an atlas, as a reference.)

☐   2.   Staple the outline map to a piece of cardboard.

☐   3.   Slide the cardboard and map into a transparent plastic bag.

☐   4.   Tape any excess plastic to the underside of the cardboard with transparent tape.

☐   5.   Stir together a salt and flour mixture (two parts salt to one part flour.) Add water until the mixture has a consistency of bread dough. (Note: Various mixtures could be substituted for the salt and flour. For instance, sawdust and liquid flour paste, or liquid starch and detergent (four tablespoons of liquid starch to one cup of powdered detergent could be used).

☐   6.   Spread a thin layer of the mixture over the entire map, beginning to shape coastlines, to carve rivers, and so forth.

☐   7.   Allow the first layer to dry overnight.

☐   8.   Apply additional layers of the mixture to build mountains, plateaus, and so forth.

☐   9.   When the relief map is completely dry, paint it with tempera paints. Use standard international map colors (for instance, green for lowlands, yellow and orange for plateaus, and brown for mountains).

☐   10.   Apply a piece of black tape along the edge of the cardboard, allowing about one-fourth inch of it to show. Your relief map will now have a finished look.

☐   11.   Display the map in an appropriate area of your classroom.

2.41   What are some of the advantages of relief maps over other kinds of maps?

_____

_____

Topographic maps. Topographic maps are used to show various natural and man-made features. As in all maps, the symbols used in topographic maps are explained in a key or legend. Topographic maps attempt to describe the three-dimensional surface of the earth on a two-dimensional flat surface. For instance, to describe elevation a topographic map may use contour lines. The reader is then able to understand the height of mountains or the elevation of cities. Different colors are often used on a topographic map to distinguish certain areas, such as green for a forest. In describing the various types of landforms, some topographic maps may become very specific, showing even houses and telephone lines.

Write *true* or *false.*

2.42 _____ Another name for a map key is a legend.
2.43 _____ A topographic map contains different colors.
2.44 _____ Contour lines describe population flow.
2.45 _____ Some topographic maps are more specific than others.
2.46 _____ Most topographic maps omit natural and man-made features.
2.47 _____ Topographic maps describe two-dimensional features on a three-dimensional surface.

USE OF MAPS

Now that you have examined various kinds of maps, you need to determine the uses of maps. The best map is of no help unless it is used properly. Just as the use of proper tools can help a carpenter to build a house more quickly, so the use of maps can help you to learn about the world. One of the greatest uses of maps is the ability to portray a three-dimensional world on a two-dimensional surface. Such representations help us to visualize physical geography. Through the use of maps, geographical locations and relationships are learned. Maps also help to locate precisely an event on the earth's surface through the use of latitudinal and longitudinal lines. All that can be said of geographical maps is also true of God's map, the Bible. The Bible locates us just where we are—sinners who need a Saviour. God's Word, then, continually guides us through life by showing us where we are as Christians and where we could or should be. The Bible represents the world as it really is—from God's point of view! The world of fallen humanity is valuable to God. You, as a part of this world, are so valuable that God gave His only Son, Jesus, so that you might have eternal life. Everything may pass away, but God's Word, His map for man, will never pass away!

Visualizing physical geography. Maps greatly help to describe the physical geography of an area. Although physical geography no longer presents the obstacles to man it once did, it is, nevertheless, important. Airplanes have conquered dangerous mountainous travel; irrigation has conquered arid deserts; improved agricultural methods have conquered nonproductive regions. A knowledge of physical features enables you to understand how geography has affected man's history. Physical features shown on a map serve to provide a basis for interpretation of man's location. Certain physical features have invited settlement. Many of today's great cities, such as Minneapolis, are located near waterfalls and the basins of great rivers. Other physical features, such as high mountains and rocky coasts, have served to discourage settlement. Some physical features, such as rivers and plains, have tended to encourage movement; other features, such as rivers and plains, have tended to encourage movement; other features such as oceans and mountains, have discouraged movement by serving as barriers. Physical features greatly affect the climate of a region by serving as windbreaks or various other agents.

Write the letter of the correct answer in the blank.

2.48   Maps describe _____ .
a. haphazardly
b. physical geography
c. geometry
d. processes

2.49   Physical features, such as _____ , discourage settlement.
a. river basins
b. mountains
c. palm trees
d. valleys

2.50   Mountains, serving as windbreaks, affect the _____ of a region.
a. climate
b. population
c. location
d. buildings

2.51   Many of today's great cities are located near _____ .
a. deserts
b. straits
c. the equator
d. waterfalls

2.52   The oceans serve as a natural _____ to movement.
a. invitation
b. encouragement
c. barrier
d. bridge

Learning geographical locations and relationships. Through the use of maps, we learn to recognize the size and shape of the world in which we live. Maps help to fix in our minds the names and locations of the places we study. Through a constant exposure to maps and globes, you can recognize a geographical area merely by its outline. Certain states and continents are seen to be adjacent, and others are recognized as being separated by great barriers and distances. The understanding of geographical relationships that the use of maps can bring results in greater understanding of world events. To realize that Israel and Egypt are neighboring countries helps us to understand why constant conflict exists between those nations. To see the closeness of Chine to Russia causes you to understand why tension may exist between these two nations. To see the great distance that separates west Texas from east Texas helps you to understand why various climates can be present in the state at the same time.

Complete this activity.

2.53   Locate on a map a state that neighbors your state. List the name of the state, and write three reasons why the two states could experience conflict and three reasons why they could experience cooperation.
a. My neighboring state is _____ .

b. Three reasons why my state and our neighbor may experience conflict are

_____ ,

_____ , and

_____ .

c. Three reasons why my state and our neighbor may experience cooperation

are _____ ,

_____ , and

_____ .

God's work has much use for maps. During the time when Jesus walked upon earth, man's geographical knowledge was limited. Today, man is able to map his entire world. The countries of the world should not represent merely land masses to us; they should represent people. When we look at a map of the world, we should learn to pray for world evangelism. Jesus taught His disciples to pray (Matthew 6:10), "Thy kingdom come. Thy will be done *in earth*. . . ." You can "visit" every country in the world through prayer. If you prayed for thirty nations every day, in one week's time you would have visited all of the two hundred ten nations of the world. Remember, a map of the world represents nearly 4 billion people who need to know Jesus Christ as their personal Lord and Saviour.

Establishing location through the use of latitude and longitude. Occasionally a person needs to know the location of an exact point on the earth's surface. Such a point is located through the use of latitude and longitude. The earth has been arbitrarily divided with lines. The north-south lines on a map or globe are called meridians, or longitudinal lines. The east-west lines are called parallels, or latitudinal lines. Because the equator is midway between the North Pole and the South Pole, it is 0º (zero degrees) latitude. The latitude at the poles is 90º. This 90º reading is obtained by realizing that the earth or any circle has a **circumference** of 360º. The distance from the equator to a pole is one-fourth the circumference; therefore, the distance is 90º. Since the earth has a circumference of approximately twenty-five thousand miles, each degree of latitude must equal almost seventy miles in length (twenty-five thousand miles divided by 360 degrees).

Because the earth has no East Pole nor West Pole, no natural line, such as the equator, exists to divide the earth into an eastern and a western half. For this reason an arbitrary line, the meridian of Greenwich, was chosen and designated as 0 degrees longitude. This imaginary line running from the North Pole and dividing the world into eastern and western halves runs through the little town of Greenwich, England, located just outside of London. The longitude of any point on earth is measured east or west from the meridian of Greenwich.

Complete this activity and answer the questions.

2.54

Latitude and longitude lines are used to locate a specific location or event, such as a shipwreck, on the earth's surface. Pretend that a shipwreck has just occurred off the western coast of Africa, and you must locate it. Figure 5 describes the disaster.

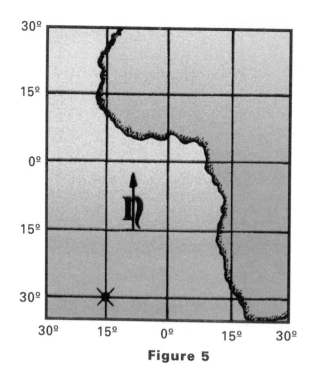

Figure 5

a. At what degree latitude did the wreck occur? _____

b. In what latitude compass direction did the wreck occur? (Hint: north or south?) _____

c. At what degree longitude did the wreck occur? _____

d. In what longitude compass direction did the wreck occur? (Hint: east or west?) _____

e. What is the exact position of the wreck?

Latitude: _____

Longitude: _____

Teacher check _____

Initial   Date

Review the material in this section in preparation for the Self Test. This Self Test will check your mastery of this particular section as well as your knowledge of the previous section.

SELF TEST 2

Match these items (each answer, 2 points).

2.01 _____ topographic map

2.02 _____ outline map

2.03 _____ sketch map

2.04 _____ distribution map

2.05 _____ pictorial map

2.06 _____ road map

2.07 _____ relief map

a. highways

b. numbers

c. contour lines

d. decorative

e. geographical shape

f. quick

g. three-dimensional

h. parallels

Write the letter of the correct answer in the blank (each answer, 2 points).

2.08   A map is an important tool of a _____ .
- a. physician
- b. geographer
- c. geologist
- d. philanthropist

2.09   Mountains have served to _____ settlement.
- a. ignore
- b. encourage
- c. discourage
- d. describe

2.010   Oceans are a natural _____ .
- a. barrier
- b. nuisance
- c. bridge
- d. disaster

2.011   The line that divides the Northern Hemisphere from the Southern Hemisphere is the _____ .
- a. prime meridian
- b. longitude
- c. 180th meridian
- d. equator

2.012   Meridians are lines that run _____ .
- a. north and south
- b. in and out
- c. around and over
- d. east and west

2.013   The equator is _____ latitude.
- a. 90 degrees
- b. 360 degrees
- c. 0 degrees
- d. $23\frac{1}{2}$ degrees

2.014   The line(s) that divide(s) the Eastern Hemisphere from the Western Hemisphere is (are) the _____ .
- a. prime meridian
- b. equator
- c. 180th meridian
- d. a and c

2.015   The most accurate representation of the earth is the _____ .
- a. relief map
- b. topographic map
- c. azimuthal equidistant projection map

2.016   You may see a corn stalk on a _____ map of Nebraska.
- a. sketch
- b. pictorial
- c. new
- d. contour

2.017   An outline map requires you to fill in _____ .
- a. details
- b. applications
- c. questions
- d. electives

Complete these statements (each answer, 3 points).

2.018   A map's symbols are explained in its _____ .

2.019   When curved surfaces are represented on flat surfaces, distances are

         _____ .

2.020   A tool that helps us visualize a landscape is a _____ .

2.021   A method of transferring portions of the globe to a flat map is a _____

         _____ .

2.022   Distances on a map can be determined by use of the _____ .

2.023   A map that you can make with a raised surface is a _____ map.

2.024   Another name for a latitudinal line is a _____ .

2.025   Minneapolis is an example of a city that is located near a _____ ,
         a natural feature.

2.026   A natural feature, such as a mountain, could serve as a _____ .

2.027   Features may be described with color on a _____ map.

Write *true* **or** *false* (each answer, 1 point).

2.028   _____   The analemma shows the difference between clock time and sun time.

2.029   _____   A great circle divides the earth into two equal halves.

2.030   _____   The equator has a diameter of approximately seven thousand nine
                           hundred miles.

2.031   _____   Hawaii is in the Pacific time zone.

2.032   _____   The earth rotates once every year.

2.033   _____   The analemma shows the longitude at which the sun will be directly
                           overhead at noon on specific dates.

2.034   _____   The International Date Line runs along the entire 180th meridian.

2.035   _____   Greenwich, England, lies on 0 degrees longitude.

2.036   _____   The earth revolves once every year.

Answer these questions (each answer, 5 points).

2.037   What is the position of Viti Levu in
         Fiji?

         Latitude: _____

         Longitude: _____

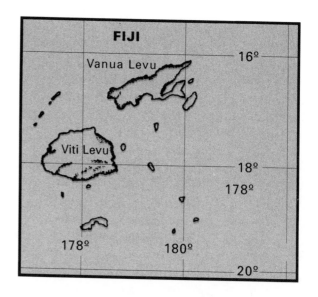

2.038   What is the combined population of states A and C? _____

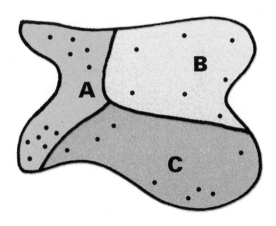

Key: • = 50,000 People

2.039   What is the distance from Tucson to Flagstaff? _____

Flagstaff •

ARIZONA

Tucson •

```
0    100   200   300
|||||||||||
```
Statute Miles

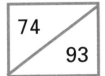

74 / 93

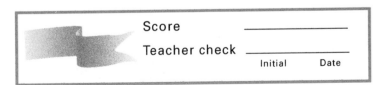

III. THE EARTH IN SYMBOL FORM—GRAPHS AND CHARTS

Graphs and charts are a way of organizing information into a clear and understandable form. Facts, figures, and **statistics** can be confusing if not properly organized and presented. To understand relationships between the statistics would also be difficult without the use of graphs and charts. Graphs and charts help to convince the reader by picturing what is otherwise hard to visualize. These visual aids make the comparison of data an easy matter.

SECTION OBJECTIVES

Read these objectives to learn what you should be able to do when you have completed this section.

7. To state a purpose of graphs and charts,
8. To list the different kinds of graphs,
9. To describe two qualities of an effective chart, and
10. To identify three sources of geographic material found in a library.

VOCABULARY

Study these words to enhance your learning success in this section.

axis (ak´ sis). A central line around which the parts of a thing are regularly arranged; a graph has an x and a y axis.

intersect (in tur sekt´). To cross each other; to divide into two parts by passing through.

statistics (stu tis´ tiks). Numerical facts assembled and classified so as to present significant information.

GRAPHS

Graphs serve to make the comparison of data possible. Many kinds of graphs exist. No one kind of graph is best because each graph serves a different purpose. The type of information to be presented will determine the type of graph to be used. Care must be exercised to learn and select the right type of graph for the right information. If done properly, the making and the reading of graphs can be enjoyable.

Purposes of graphs. Graphs are a type of visual aid. They are used to make important facts clear and illustrate relationships that are difficult to see. The relationships are shown through the use of the comparison of data. Generally, the items being compared are shown on a graph with one vertical **axis** and one horizontal axis. The graph material could also be shown in picture or circle form. The value of a graph is determined by its usefulness. Therefore, no best type of graph exists. Graphs serve to help develop critical thinking by the organized presentation of factual material. Graphs are an important part of geography.

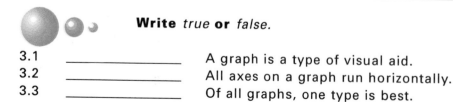

Write *true* **or** *false.*

3.1 _____ A graph is a type of visual aid.

3.2 _____ All axes on a graph run horizontally.

3.3 _____ Of all graphs, one type is best.

| 3.4 | _____ | Graphs show relationships through the use of comparison. |
| 3.5 | _____ | Graphs have little to do with the organization of material. |

Types of graphs. A pictograph uses pictures or symbols to describe information. Such a presentation is clear and simple. Only approximate, rather than exact, amounts can be shown on the pictograph. The pictures or symbols used are easily associated with what they represent. The symbols are consistent in size and shape, and they represent the same amount.

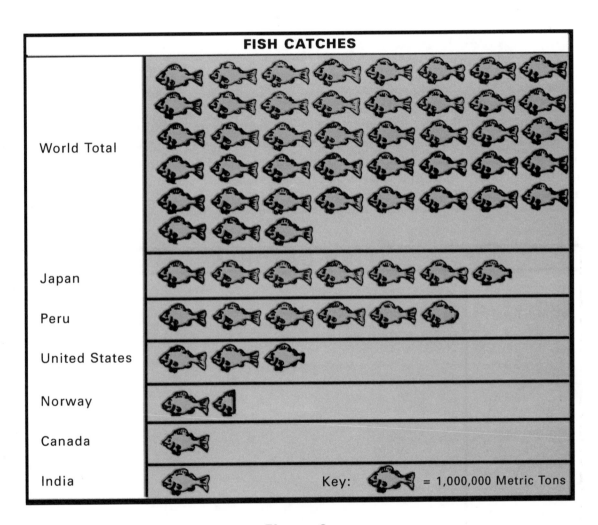

Figure 6

Write the letter of the correct answer in the blank. Refer to Figure 6.

3.6   Japan caught million metric tons of fish.
    a. $6\frac{1}{2}$
    b. $2\frac{1}{2}$
    c. 1
    d. $8\frac{1}{2}$

3.7   The nations catching the least amount of fish were _____ .
    a. United States and Canada
    b. Peru and Norway
    c. India and Peru
    d. Canada and India

3.8   Peru caught one million metric tons less of fish than _____ .
    a. the United States
    b. Canada
    c. Japan
    d. Norway

3.9   The nation that relies most heavily on fishing appears to be _____ .
    a. Norway
    b. Japan
    c. Canada
    d. United States

A broken bar graph is a further development of a pictograph. The pictures or symbols are replaced with a bar broken into pieces of uniform size. As with the symbol, one standardized section of bar represents a unit of measurement. Information is easily read from such a graph. The various lengths of broken bars on the graph make the comparison of data obvious.

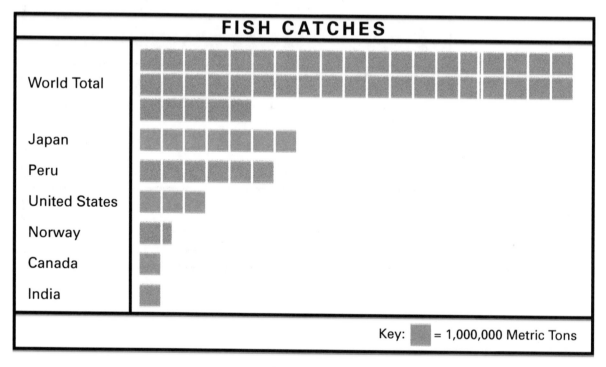

Figure 7

Bar graphs are the result of further refinement of broken bar graphs. The bars on this graph are not broken into small, uniform sizes. The bars are now solid and continuous. The bars may appear on the graph either in a horizontal or a vertical position.

The most accurate of all graphs is the line graph. Another name for the line graph is the trend graph. The line graph can be used to show changes that occur over periods of time. How steeply the line goes up or comes down is called the line's slope. Line graphs have different uses from bar graphs, although both are used for comparisons. Bar graphs are used to compare different quantities at the same point in time. Line graphs are used to compare increases and decreases in a quantity over a period of time. Information can be found in the line graph be determining where the horizontal and vertical axes **intersect**.

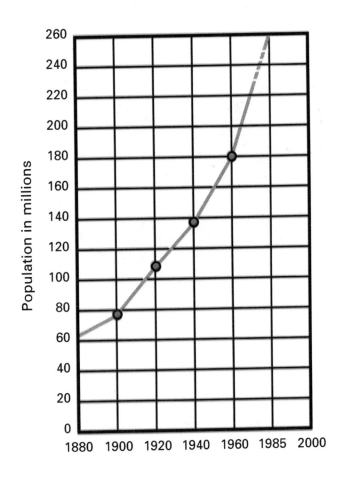

Figure 8

Answer these questions. Refer to Figure 8.

3.10   What is the vertical axis labeled? _____

3.11   What was the United States population in 1940? _____

3.12   What is the difference between the 1900 and the 1920 population figures?

_____

3.13   What is the year of lowest population listed on this line graph? _____

Circle graphs show how parts relate to one another and how all parts relate to the whole. The parts of a circle graph resemble wedges or pieces of pie. Because of their appearance, circle graphs have been called pie graphs. Circle graphs are easy to make and to read, but they are not as accurate as line graphs. Figures used in the circle graph must be converted to fractions or percentages to be shown as pieces of the whole. The whole circle represents 100 per cent; thus, all percentages of the pieces must add to 100 per cent.

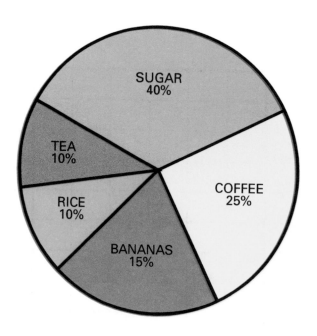

Figure 9

 **Answer these questions.** Refer to Figure 9.

3.14   Do all pieces of the circle add to 100 per cent? _____
3.15   Bananas are what per cent of total products grown? _____
3.16   Which product is grown more than any other? _____

Cautions concerning graphs. When making or using graphs, several points must be remembered. All factors of the graph must contribute to geographical understanding. Graphs must be simple, meaningful, attractive, and accurate, and they must present their material clearly. Graphs must be labeled with a simple but descriptive title. The vertical and horizontal scales or axes of a graph must be plainly labeled and divided into appropriate units. Most graphs begin with a base level of zero to make comparisons easier. If symbols or pictures are used in a graph, they must be explained in a key or legend. The information presented in a graph should be logical and easily understood. If reference books are used as a source of information, credit should be given. Through the use of graphs, information is presented clearly and readers are convinced of geographical truths.

Write *true* or *false.*

3.17 _____ The most accurate graph is the line graph.

3.18 _____ Graph symbols are explained in a key.

3.19 _____ Graph titles are seldom both simple and descriptive.

3.20 _____ Most graphs do not begin at a base level of zero.

3.21 _____ Circle graphs are also called pie graphs.

Complete this activity.

3.22 List the different kinds of graphs.

a. _____   d. _____

b. _____   e. _____

c. _____

CHARTS

The information gathered in a study of the earth's surface can be presented in charts. Charts, like graphs, are means of summarizing geographical knowledge in symbol or written form. Effective charts have two specific qualities: the organization of information and the clarification of understanding of what is being studied. As useful as charts are, special cautions must be considered in making and reading charts.

Purposes of charts. Charts have many uses in geography. Some geographic charts show relationships; other charts, such as flow charts, describe simple processes. Charts can summarize information about cities, countries, resources, and products. Through the use of a chart, information can often be presented more clearly and quickly than in other ways. A chart is only effective if it can present information in a clear, concise, and effective manner.

The three major types of charts include charts of relationships, flow charts, and charts of summarization. Of the three types, charts that show relationships are the most effective. These charts are often illustrated for clarity. Charts of relationships may illustrate, for instance, the manufacture of steel by showing that it is related to coal deposits, iron ore deposits, limestone deposits, and water supplies.

To describe the major steps in the processing of a product, a flow chart would be used. For example, an illustrated chart tracing grains of wheat from the field to the table would include the field, the grain elevator, the flour mill, the bakery, the retail store, and the table.

Charts are also used to summarize learned material. Such a chart could show the land formation of a region, the exports of a nation, or the uses of a product.

Answer these questions.

3.23 What are the three major types of charts?

a. _____

b. _____

c. _____

3.24 Which type of chart is the most effective?

_____

3.25 Which type of chart would describe the steps in the processing of a product?

_____

3.26 What are two qualities of an effective chart?

a. _____

b. _____

Cautions concerning charts. When making and using charts, their main purpose must always be remembered: to present information in a short, simple manner. Heeding several cautions will help further this goal. Charts should be attractive, having a sense of balance, proportion, and color harmony. Keep all charts simple; avoid adding too much information. Make certain that charts are clearly legible and are large enough to be easily seen. Be sure that the chart organizes the information in the best possible manner. Most readers enjoy encountering a meaningful, attractive chart. Such a visual aid heightens the study of geography.

Complete this activity and answer these questions.

3.27 Design a chart, using materials of your own choosing that will either show relationships, describe the steps in a process, or summarize information. Display your chart in the appropriate area of the classroom.

a. Which type of chart did you choose to make?

_____

b. How does your chart help to present information?

_____

OTHER RESOURCE MATERIAL

Other resource material is available that will help in your study of geography. Your teacher can help you to find just the right resource for your particular need.

Location of resource material. Perhaps the first area to check in your search for geographic resources is the card catalog of your school or public library. Look under the heading *Geography,* and make a list of available resources. You will find that many of the resources are classified as reference materials. This classification means that you may not check these resources out, but you must use them in the library. You may already have some geographic reference materials in your classroom.

Types of resource material. The most commonly used resource is the encyclopedia. The topics are listed alphabetically in the encyclopedia; thus, you may turn right to the topic of your geographic concern. Another very common source of information is the dictionary.

Besides listing its contents alphabetically, the dictionary also contains valuable tables and charts in the back. A variety of books are available to help you locate **statistical** information. Such sources include *Statistical Abstract of the United States, The Commodity Yearbook, The Agricultural Yearbook, The Statesman's Yearbook, The World Almanac, The South American Handbook,* and *The Statistical Yearbook of the United Nations.* In addition to books you will find many magazines to be helpful. Your teacher or librarian can help you locate and use the *Reader's Guide To Periodical Literature.* In this guide, published yearly, you will find a listing of a wide range of topics. The listing states in which magazine an article was published and identifies the particular issue. On a slip of paper, write the information given in the guide, and take the paper to the librarian so that she may locate the magazine for you. To help you visualize geographic areas, an atlas can be used. An atlas is simply a book of maps. A variety of these books exists, covering everything from highways to the world. A world atlas, together with a globe, can give you a good picture of the world in which we live.

God is the author of geography. No land feature exists that God did not create. Your careful study of geography should result in a greater appreciation for God. Perhaps the Apostle Paul was thinking of this result when he said (Romans 1:20), ". . . the invisible things of him from the creation of the world are clearly seen, being understood by the things that are made, even his eternal power and God-head. . . ."

To truly appreciate geography, a person needs faith. Faith enables one to see and to appreciate not only the creation but also the Creator. Studying geography, the Christian can say from his heart (Hebrews 11:3), "Through faith we understand that the worlds were framed by the word of God, so that things which are seen were not made of things which do appear."

Complete this activity.

3.28   List three sources of geographic material found in a library.

a. _____

b. _____

c. _____

Answer these questions.

3.29   A book of maps is called a(n) _____ .

3.30   The most commonly used resource is a(n) _____ .

3.31   Books you cannot check out of a library are called _____ .

Teacher check _____
                        Initial   Date

Before you take this last Self Test, you may want to do one or more of these self checks.

1. _____   Read the objectives. Determine if you can do them.
2. _____   Restudy the material related to any objectives that you cannot do.
3. _____   Use the SQ3R study procedure to review the material:
   a.   **S**can the sections,
   b.   **Q**uestion yourself again (review the questions you wrote initially),
   c.   **R**ead to answer your questions,
   d.   **R**ecite the answers to yourself, and
   e.   **R**eview areas you did not understand.
4. _____   Review all vocabulary, activities, and Self Tests, writing a correct answer for every wrong answer.

SELF TEST 3

Complete these statements (each answer, 3 points).

3.01   Graphs and charts are a form of _____ aid.

3.02   The most commonly used resource is an _____ .

3.03   The most accurate graph is the _____ graph.

3.04   Another name for a pie graph is a _____ graph.

3.05   Most graphs begin with a base level of _____ .

3.06   A book of maps is called an _____ .

3.07   The chart that is the most effective is the _____ chart.

3.08   The steps in the processing of a product would be described in a _____ chart.

3.09   A key explains the _____ of a graph.

3.010   Graphs show relationships through the use of _____ .

Match these items (each answer, 2 points).

3.011 _____ great circle

3.012 _____ analemma

3.013 _____ rotation

3.014 _____ revolution

3.015 _____ prime meridian

3.016 _____ relief map

3.017 _____ outline map

3.018 _____ distribution

3.019 _____ pictorial map

3.020 _____ topographic map

a. 0 degrees

b. contour lines

c. orbit

d. equator

e. three-dimensional

f. globe

g. axis

h. numbers

i. geographical shape

j. sun time

k. decorative

Write the letter of the correct answer in the blank (each answer, 2 points).

3.021   To gather geographic facts you generally would not consult _____ .
- a. an encyclopedia
- b. a phone directory
- c. a dictionary
- d. the Statistical Yearbook of the United Nations

3.022   Graphs and charts make the _____ of data an easy matter.
- a. omission
- b. union
- c. comparison
- d. finding

3.023   The line that runs generally along the 180th meridian is the _____ .
- a. equator
- b. International Date Line
- c. prime meridian
- d. Tropic of Capricorn

3.024   The equator is located at _____ longitude.
         a. 0 degrees
         b. 90 degrees
         c. 360 degrees
         d. neither a, b, nor c
3.025   When curved surfaces are represented on flat surfaces, distances are _____ .
         a. distorted
         b. accurate
         c. inverted
         d. lengthened
3.026   The Prime Meridian is in the _____ Hemisphere.
         a. Eastern
         b. Western
         c. Northern
         d. Southern
         e. a and b
         f. c and d
3.027   Physical features on a topographic map may be described with _____ .
         a. words
         b. pictures
         c. colors
         d. scales
3.028   A map that is drawn quickly is a _____ map.
         a. California
         b. distribution
         c. sketch
         d. road
3.029   A mountain could serve as a _____ .
         a. barrier
         b. windbreak
         c. boundary
         d. a, b, and c
3.030   An important tool of the geographer is a _____ .
         a. map
         b. pick
         c. analemma
         d. parallel

Write *true* **or** *false* (each answer, 1 point).
3.031   _____   The Tropic of Cancer is a great circle.
3.032   _____   The earth is tilted.
3.033   _____   A time belt is 15 degrees of latitude wide.
3.034   _____   The globe is a perfect sphere.
3.035   _____   Azimuthal equidistant projection maps are used to determine great-
                             circle routes.

3.036	_____	The United States is in the Western Hemisphere.
3.037	_____	Oceans are natural barriers to travel.
3.038	_____	Many major cities are located near rivers and waterfalls.
3.039	_____	Some distribution maps use dots.
3.040	_____	You may see a corn stalk on a pictorial map of Alaska.

Answer these questions (each answer, 5 points).

3.041   What are the five kinds of graphs?

_____

_____

3.042   What are the two qualities of an effective chart?

_____

_____

3.043   What is wrong with this circle graph?

_____

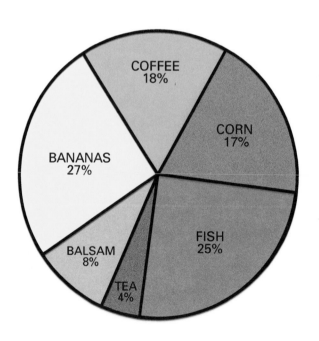

3.044   What are three sources of geographic material found in a library?

_____

_____

_____

_____

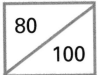
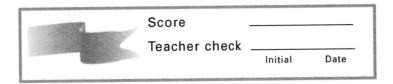

Before taking the LIFEPAC Test, you may want to do one or more of these self checks.

1. _____ Read the objectives. Check to see if you can do them.
2. _____ Restudy the material related to any objectives that you cannot do.
3. _____ Use the SQ3R study procedure to review the material.
4. _____ Review activities, Self Tests, and LIFEPAC vocabulary words.
5. _____ Restudy areas of weakness indicated by the last Self Test.

NOTES